KT Tunstall
Eye to the Telescope

WISE PUBLICATIONS
part of The Music Sales Group
London / New York / Paris / Sydney / Copenhagen / Berlin / Madrid / Tokyo

Published by
Wise Publications,
8/9 Frith Street, London, W1D 3JB, England.

Exclusive distributors:
Music Sales Limited,
Distribution Centre, Newmarket Road, Bury St Edmunds,
Suffolk, IP33 3YB, England.

Music Sales Pty Limited,
120 Rothschild Avenue, Rosebery,
NSW 2018, Australia.

Order No. AM92234
ISBN 0-7119-4359-1
This book © Copyright 2005 by Wise Publications,
a division of Music Sales Limited.

Music arranged by Derek Jones.
Music processed by Paul Ewers Music Design.
Edited by Lucy Holliday.

Printed in the United Kingdom.

www.musicsales.com

Your Guarantee of Quality:
As publishers, we strive to produce every book
to the highest commercial standards.

The music has been freshly engraved. Particular care has
been given to specifying acid-free, neutral-sized paper made from
pulps which have not been elemental chlorine bleached.

This pulp is from farmed sustainable forests
and was produced with special regard for the environment.

Throughout, the printing and binding have been planned to ensure a
sturdy, attractive publication which should give years of enjoyment.

If your copy fails to meet our high standards, please inform us
and we will gladly replace it.

Other Side Of The World

Words by KT Tunstall
Music by KT Tunstall & Martin Terefe

the wa - ter.

2. All the mus-cles tight-en in her face, bu-ries her soul
(3.) on comes the pa-nic light, hold-ing on with fin-gers and feel-ings a-like

in one em-brace. They're one and the same,
But the time has come to move

just like wa-ter.
a - long.

1° only

And the fire fades a-way

Another Place To Fall

Words & Music by KT Tunstall

smile, you should try it just once in a while. Ba - by it's not quite
swal - low. Men who have ru - ined your life, you con - sume them with mi - ni - mum

your style, (it's) sim - ply too ea - sy to do, and you might not see it
strife. But now you have got in - di - ges - tion, the ant - a - cid comes__

through. See it though.__
__ as a ques - tion.

13

14

Am

There is-n't much more I can say,

Bm

I don't un-der-stand the de-

Am

-lay. You're ask-ing for friend-ly ad- vice_____ and re-main-ing in per-ma-nent

Bm⁷

Am

cri- sis.____ Af- fec- tion is yours if you ask.

Bm

First you must take off your

Am

mask.

B⁷

When your back's turned I've de-cid- ed____ I'll throw it a-way just like

16

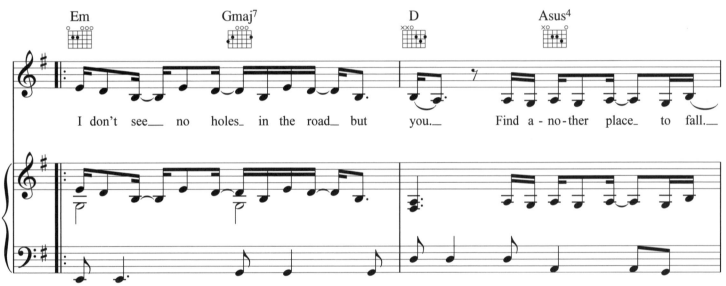

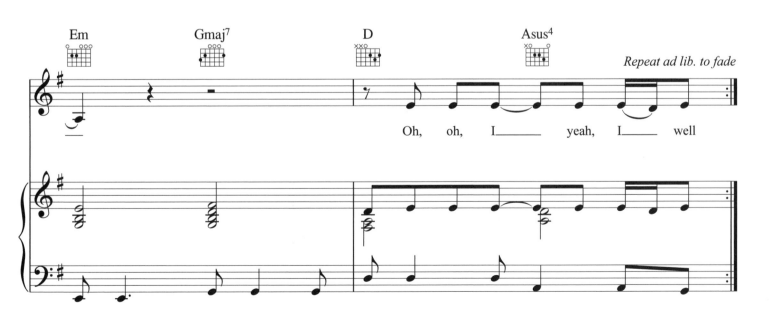

Under The Weather

Words by KT Tunstall
Music by KT Tunstall & Tommy D

1. Un - der this na - tion - al rain - cloud____

still feel like I'm gon-na sink. Coz I'm under the wea-ther
cut like a sword in your side? Coz you're

just like the world, so sor-ry for be-ing so bold.
2° + 3° and I need some-bo-dy to hold.

When I turn out the light you're out of sight, al-though

I know that I'm not a - lone, it feels like

Suddenly I See

Words & Music by KT Tunstall

I can see her eyes look-ing from a page in a ma-ga-zine. She makes_ me feel_ like I could be a tow-er. Big_ strong tow-er, yeah._ The pow-er to be,_ the pow-er to give, the pow-er to see,_ yeah, yeah._ (Sud-den-ly I

Miniature Disasters

Words & Music by KT Tunstall

1. I don't want to be se - cond best, don't wan-na
(2.) hot and cold, got to be
(3.) raise my voice don't have to be

Silent Sea

Words by KT Tunstall
Music by KT Tunstall & Jimmy Hogarth

Universe & U

Words by KT Tunstall
Music by KT Tunstall & Pleasure

False Alarm

Words by KT Tunstall
Music by KT Tunstall & Martin Terefe

Con pedale

1. I'm try-ing to put__ this thing to bed, I've drugged it in its
(2.) up, the au - di - ence is

sleep. There is - n't ma - ny me - mo - ries__ I'm com - fort - able__ to keep.
still. I'm strug - gl - ing__ to ca - ter for__ the space I'm meant__ to fill.

1.

2. And now the cur - tain's com - ing

2.

I'm try - ing to put___ this thing___ to

G

Gmaj⁷

bed. I drugged it in its sleep. Re - mem - ber what___ you

Am⁷

D⁷

D⁶

said. Are you com - fort - able to keep it?

D⁷

D⁶

Fmaj⁷

E

Keep it?

Heal Over

Words & Music by KT Tunstall

53

Stoppin' The Love

Words by KT Tunstall
Music by KT Tunstall & Tommy D

You got me look-ing up_____ ev-en when I'm fall-ing____ down.____

You got me crawl-ing_____ out_____ of my skin._____

You got me won-der-ing____ why_____ I am un-der-neath_ this

big old sky,___ stop-ping the lov-ing get-ting in.____

To Coda ⊕

Through The Dark

Words by KT Tunstall
Music by KT Tunstall & Martin Terefe

65

Black Horse And The Cherry Tree

Words & Music by KT Tunstall

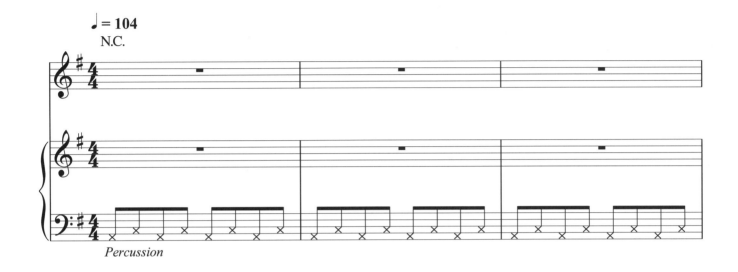

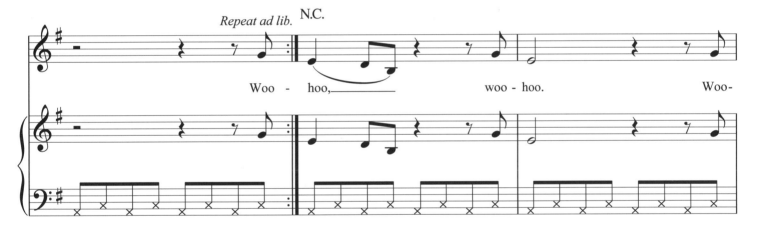

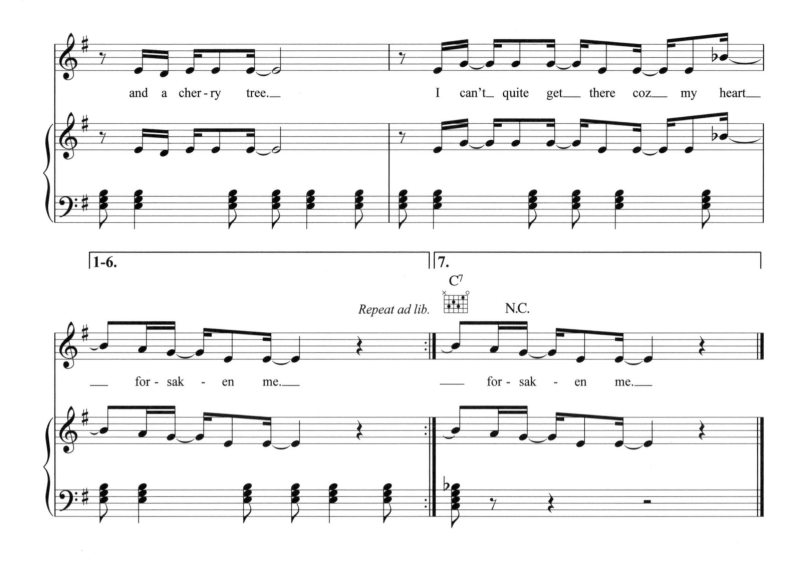

Verse 3:

And my heart hit a problem in the early hours
So I stopped it dead for a beat or two
But I cut some cord and I shouldn't have done it
And it won't forgive me after all these years.

Verse 4:

So I sent her to a place in the middle of nowhere
With a big black horse and a cherry tree
It won't come back, coz it's oh so happy
And now I've got a hole for the world to see.

3456789
12/05(57117)